SATs Skills

Maths Workbook

Numbers

10–11 years

UNIVERSITY PRESS

OXFORD
UNIVERSITY PRESS

Great Clarendon Street, Oxford, OX2 6DP, United Kingdom

Oxford University Press is a department of the University of Oxford.
It furthers the University's objective of excellence in research, scholarship,
and education by publishing worldwide. Oxford is a registered trade mark
of Oxford University Press in the UK and in certain other countries

Text and illustrations © Oxford University Press 2017
Author: Andrew Baines

British Library Cataloguing in Publication Data
Data available

978-0-19-274964-2

10 9 8 7 6 5 4 3 2

Paper used in the production of this book is a natural, recyclable product
made from wood grown in sustainable forests. The manufacturing process
conforms to the environmental regulations of the country of origin.

Printed in China

Acknowledgements

Cover illustration: Lo Cole
Page make-up and illustrations by Aptara

Although we have made every effort to trace and contact all copyright
holders before publication this has not been possible in all cases. If notified,
the publisher will rectify any errors or omissions at the earliest opportunity.

Links to third party websites are provided by Oxford in good faith and for
information only. Oxford disclaims any responsibility for the materials
contained in any third party website referenced in this work.

Algebra: simple formulae

> ### 💡 Helpful Hint
>
> Sharing is the same as dividing. We use a fraction to show the division with algebra.
>
> **Examples**
>
> **1** Three apples cost 67p. Express this **algebraically**.
>
> **Answer:** $3x = 67$
>
> **2** Two lots of a number plus 5 is equal to ten. Express this algebraically.
>
> **Answer:** $2x + 5 = 10$
>
> **3** We share some sweets equally between 6 people. Express this algebraically.
>
> **Answer:** $\frac{x}{6}$

Ⓐ Answer these questions. You do not need to show your workings out.

1 5 identical toys cost £26
Express this algebraically.

_____ [1]

2 I have some books and after giving away 6 I have 14 books left.
Express this algebraically.

_____ [1]

3 If you share a prize of £p between 7 people equally they each get £12
Express this algebraically.

_____ [1]

4 I received a gift of £g from my Gran. I spent £5 and now have £20
Express this algebraically.

_____ [1]

5 I want 6 equal lengths of material and an extra 10 cm. The total length has to come to 5.6 m.
Express this algebraically.

_____ [1]

5

Example

The formula for the **perimeter** of a square is $P = 4x$.
Find the value of P when $x = 6$.

Answer: $P = 4x$

$\quad\quad\quad = 4(6)$ Substitute the x for 6. Place it in a pair of brackets in case you have any negative/minus signs.

$\quad\quad\quad = 4 \times 6$ If a number is in front of a pair of brackets it means that you need that many "*times*" the number.

$\quad P = 24$

Ⓑ Answer these questions. You do not need to show your workings out.

1 Find the value of M if $M = p + 5$ and $p = 9$

_____ [1]

2 Find the value of L if $L = m - 4$ and $m = 27$

_____ [1]

3 Find the value of P if $P = 8g$ and $g = 4$

_____ [1]

4 Find the value of B if $B = \dfrac{C}{3}$ and $C = 24$

_____ [1]

Ⓒ Answer these questions.

1 A square with sides of x cm has a perimeter of 20 cm. Find the value of x and show your working out.

Show your workings

cm

[1]

5

2 Match the following sentences to the algebra expressions and equations.

| Share £x between seven people. Each person gets £20. | | $x + 7 = 20$ |

| Seven apples cost 20p. | | $x - 7 = 20$ |

| If you take seven away from this number you get 20. | | $7x = 20$ |

| In seven years' time I will be 20. | | $\frac{x}{7} = 20$ |

[4]

3 I think of a number, then multiply it by five. I then add twelve.
My new number is one thousand and six. Express this algebraically.

_____ [1]

4

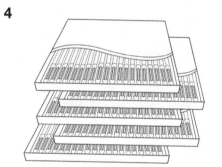

There are 24 pens in each box.
The total number of pens, T, is found using the formula $T = 24b$, where b is the number of boxes.

If $b = 5$, then what is T? Show your working out.

Show your workings

$T =$

_____ [1]

6

(D) Answer these questions. You do not need to show your workings out.

1 Find the value of Q if $Q = 2x + 4$ and $x = 0.5$ $Q =$ _____ [1]

2 Find the value of R if $R = 12 - 3y$ and $y = 2.5$ $R =$ _____ [1]

3 Find the value of P if $P = 2x - y$ and $x = 7, y = 5.1$ $P =$ _____ [1]

4 Find the value of W if $W = \frac{1}{2}x + 2y$ and $x = 9, y = 1.3$ $W =$ _____ [1]

The perimeter P of this rectangle is $6x + 16$

5 Calculate the perimeter P when $x = 1.5\,$cm. $P =$ _____ cm [1]

6 Calculate the perimeter P when $x = 13\,$cm. $P =$ _____ cm [1]

If the rectangle is actually a square, so its length is as long as its width, what is the answer to each of these questions?

7 What is the value of x?   _____ cm [1]

8 What is the length of one side of the square?   _____ cm [1]

9 What is the perimeter of the square?   _____ cm [1]

10 Give a simpler formula for the perimeter P of the square shown above, that uses x.   _____ cm [1]

10

Algebra: linear sequences

Examples

1 Find the next two numbers in the following **sequence**:

3, 4, 6, 9, 13, ... , ...

Answer:

Look to see what is being added or multiplied to get to the next **term**:

3,   4,   6,   9,   13,   ... ,   ...
   +1   +2   +3   +4   +5   +6

So the answers are 18 and 24

2 Find the next term in the sequence:

1, 1, 2, 3, 5, 8, 13, ...

Answer:

There are some special sequences:

1, 3, 6, 10, 15, ...
Triangular numbers, which form triangles where the difference between each term increases by 1 each time.

1, 4, 9, 16, 25, 36, ...
Square numbers, which forms squares and the terms are 1^2, 2^2, 3^2, 4^2, ...

1, 1, 2, 3, 5, 8, 13, ...
Fibonacci numbers which are found by adding the two previous terms.

So the answer is 21 since they are Fibonacci numbers.

3 Find a pair of numbers which satisfies the following:

I double the first number then add the second number to get a total of 10

Answer:

$2x + y$ = 10
2(0) + (10) = 10
2(1) + (8) = 10
2(2) + (6) = 10
2(3) + (4) = 10
2(4) + (2) = 10
2(5) + (0) = 10

All the above combinations work.

Unit 2

(A) Answer these questions. You do not need to show your workings out.

1 Find the next two terms in the following sequence:
5, 6, 7, 8, 9, …, …

_____ _____ [2]

2 Find the next two terms in the following sequence:
12, 15, 18, 21, 24, …, …

_____ _____ [2]

3 Find the next two terms in the following sequence:
15, 13, 11, 9, 7, …, …

_____ _____ [2]

4 Find the next two terms in the following sequence:
2, 2, 4, 6, 10, …, …

_____ _____ [2]

Circle your answers to the following questions.

5 I add the first number to three lots of the second number and the result is 10

  a 1, 2   **b** 2, 3   **c** 8, 1   **d** 5, 2   **e** 4, 2   [1]

6 I add twice the first number to the second number and the result is 14

  a 4, 5   **b** 5, 4   **c** 10, 4   **d** 4, 1   **e** 3, 4   [1]

7 I add three times the first number to two lots of the second number and the result is 13

  a 10, 3   **b** 3, 2.5   **c** 2.5, 6.5   **d** 3, 2   **e** 4, 2   [1]

(B) Answer these questions.

1

Four matches are arranged to make a square, as above. More matches are added to make 2 squares, and then 3 squares. How many matches will be needed to make 4 squares and 7 squares?

4 squares require _____ matches.
7 squares require _____ matches.

Show your workings

[2]

13

2

Two pens and two pencils cost £3.70. Which of the following prices are correct?
Circle the correct options.

a pen £1.30, pencil £0.45

b pen £1.30, pencil £0.55

c pen £1.25, pencil £0.65

d pen £1.15, pencil £0.70

e pen £1.05, pencil £0.80

Show your workings

[2]

3

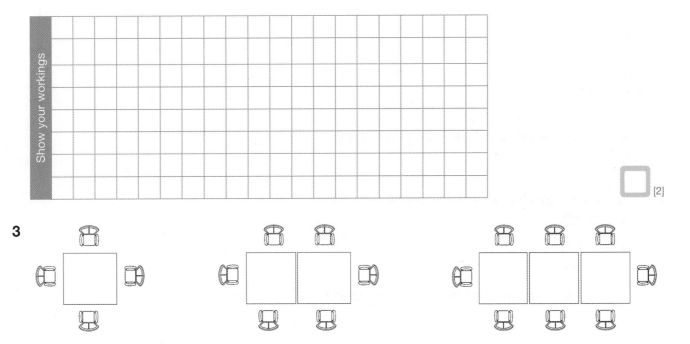

A restaurant has different arrangements of tables and chairs. Above you can see them using one, two and three tables.
How many chairs are needed with 4 tables and 10 tables?

4 tables require _____ chairs. 10 tables require _____ chairs.

Show your workings

[1]

3

4 The Bond family have three triplets at primary school and a pair of twins at secondary school. Their combined ages are 47. How old are the children?

The triplets are _____ and the twins are _____ or, the triplets are _____ and the twins are _____ .

Show your workings

[2]

ⓒ Answer these questions. You do not need to show your workings out.

1 Find the next two terms in the following sequence:
7, 5, 3, 1, ..., ...

_____ _____
[2]

2 Find the next two terms in the following sequence:
2.3, 5.2, 8.1, ..., ...

_____ _____
[2]

3 Find the next two terms in the following sequence:
3, 4, 6, 9, 13, ..., ...

_____ _____
[2]

Circle the correct answers below.

4 I add the first number to three lots of the second number and the result is 9.4

    a 6.3, 3.1   **b** 2.3, 2.2   **c** 6.1, 1.1   **d** 5.2, 1.1   **e** 1.1, 3.1
[1]

5 I add half the first number to twice the second number and the result is 8

    a 6.8, 2.3   **b** 1.7, 2.3   **c** 6.8, 4.6   **d** 10, 2   **e** 10, 1
[1]

6 I add three times the first number to half of the second number and the result is 9

    a 2, 8   **b** 3, 0   **c** 0, 4.5   **d** 2.3, 4.3   **e** 5, -6
[1]

Calculations: estimates and two-step problems

Examples

You can use estimation and inverse operations to check answers because sometimes mistakes are made with careless use of a calculator.

Here are some examples:

$15 \div 5 = 3$
$15 \div 3 = 5$
$15 = 3 \times 5$
$14.848 \div 5.12 = 2.9$
$14.848 \div 2.9 = 5.12$
$14.848 = 3 \times 5.12$

$14 - 6 = 8$
$6 = 14 - 8$
$14 = 8 + 6$

$14.57 - 6.14 = 8.43$
$6.14 = 14.57 - 8.43$
$14.57 = 8.43 + 6.14$

Use known calculations to find similar quantities.

So if we are told that $57 \times 14 = 798$
       then to find 58×14
We can just add another 14 to 798, which makes 812

(A) Answer these questions. You do not need to show your workings out.

1 $6.27 \times 5.3 = 33.231$
    $33.231 \div 5.3 =$ _____ [1]

2 Use approximation to find the correct answer from the options below:
    $101.5584 \div 11.36$

   a 89.4   **b** 894   **c** 0.894   **d** 8.94   **e** 0.00894   [1]

3 The class needs to buy 32 rulers which each cost £0.48
    Roughly how much will this cost to the nearest pound?   £ _____ [1]

4 Bea has 23 pieces of music to practise for the school show.
    She takes 2 hours 3 minutes to practise the first piece.

    If she spends the same time on each piece, approximately how
    much longer will she need to spend practising the remaining pieces? _____ [1]

4

5 Jaime wants to save up £20.99 for a game.
He has already saved £11.22 and his uncle has given him £5
How much does he still need to save?   £ _____ [1]

6 Find the missing number x in the following sequence: _____
26, 34, 42, ... , ..., x, 74, ... [1]

(B) Answer these questions and show your workings out.

1 The local swimming pool is 25 m long, 1.85 m deep and is 6 lanes wide. Each lane is 2.1 m wide.
What is the approximate volume of water in the swimming pool?
Round each length to the nearest metre.

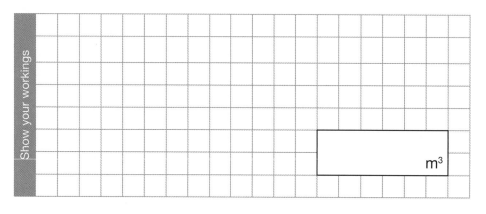

m³ [1]

2 What is 571.5 ÷ 450 + 12 − 0.27?

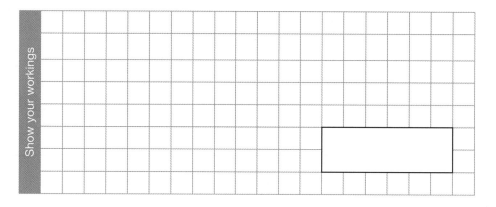

[1]

4

3 Obi has been given £8.50 to go and buy a book. He is allowed to spend the rest on sweets. The book costs £7.98.

When he gets to the shop he discovers there is an offer for £1 off the book.

How much will he have left to spend on sweets?

Show your workings

£

[1]

4 Becky has 2 hours to get ready for her triathlon race. She needs to set up her bike and running things before getting ready for the swim.

She normally takes 5 minutes to set up for the run and 25 minutes for the bike, with 20 minutes getting ready for the swim. She then spends the rest of the time relaxing.

Today she had a problem with setting up the bike so it took her 55 minutes.
How long will she have to relax today?

Show your workings

[1]

2

Unit 3

ⓒ Answer these questions. You do not need to show your workings out.

1 15.72 – 4.6 + 2.9 = 14.02

What is 14.02 – 2.9 + 4.6? _____ ☐ [1]

2 Find the approximate total cost
of 976 gearboxes which each
cost £2897.67   £ _____ ☐ [1]

3 Use approximation to find the correct answer from the options below.
What is $9.87 \times 4.9 + 2.54$?

a 50.903
b 5.93
c 509.3
d 48.25
e 60.203   ☐ [1]

4 A supermarket chain sends out 796 boxes of frozen peas to 3 stores.

The first store takes 429, the second takes 208 and the third store was going to take the rest
but they only have room for 100.

How many boxes are NOT taken by the 3 stores? _____ ☐ [1]

5 Find the missing number x in the following sequence:

26, 15, 4, ... , ..., x, ... $x =$ _____ ☐ [1]

5

Calculations: properties of number

Examples

1 Find the common **factors** of 15 and 18.

Answer:

The factors of 15 are:	**1**		**3**	5			15
The factors of 18 are:	**1**	2	**3**		6	9	18
Common factors are:	**1**		**3**				

2 Find the common **multiples** of 5 and 8.

Answer:

The multiples of 5 are:	5	10	15	20	25	30	35	**40**
The multiples of 8 are:	8	16	24	32	**40**	48		
Common multiples are:	40	80	120	…	(multiples of **40**)			

3 Identify the square, cube and **prime numbers** from the following list.
20, 21, 22, 23, 24, 25, 26, 27, 28, 29, 30

Answer:

Square numbers are:	1	4	9	16	25	36	49	64	…
Cube numbers are:	1	8	**27**	64	125	216	…		
Prime numbers are:	2	3	5	7	11	13	…	**23**	**29** …

So the square number is 25, the cube is 27 and the prime numbers are 23 and 29.

Ⓐ Answer these questions. You do not need to show your workings out.

1 What is the common factor of 8 and 15? _____ ☐ [1]

2 What are the common factors of 21 and 35? _____ ☐ [1]

3 What are the first two common multiples of 5 and 15? _____ ☐ [1]

4 What are the first two common multiples of 6 and 8? _____ ☐ [1]

4

5 Find two square numbers between 50 and 100 _____ [1]

6 Find two cube numbers between 50 and 150 _____ [1]

7 Find two prime numbers between 48 and 60 _____ [1]

Ⓑ Answer these questions.

1

A clock chimes every 15 minutes and a watch beeps every twenty minutes. They both sound at 10 o'clock. When do they both sound together before 12 o'clock?

Show your workings

[1]

2

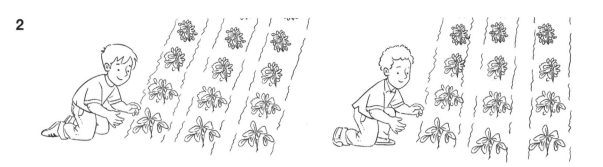

Two gardeners are planting potatoes next to each other. Jay plants 24 potato plants in equal rows and Pat plants 21 plants in equal rows. Neither plants their potatoes in a single row but they both have the same number of rows.

How many rows did they both plant?

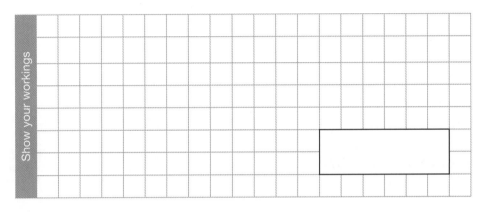

Show your workings

[1]

3 Two children share 100 cube-shaped building bricks between them. Hatti uses all her bricks to make a big cube. She then knocks them all down and makes a flat square, which is one brick high and doesn't have any bricks left.

Jonty can make a square with all his bricks, but when he makes a big cube he always has some bricks left over.

How many bricks did Jonty start with?

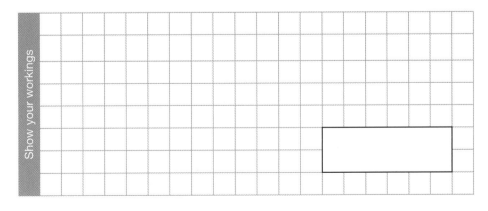

Show your workings

[1]

2

4 Class 5D has at least 10 boys and 10 girls but there are fewer than 28 children in total. The teacher tries to split the boys up into equal groups but cannot because there is always a boy on his own. The teacher then tries with the girls but has the same problem.

There are more girls than boys.

How many boys are in Class 5D?

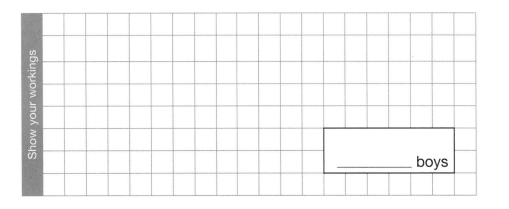

_____ boys

[2]

ⓒ Answer these questions. You do not need to show your workings out.

1 What are the common factors of 24 and 105? _____ [1]

2 What are the common factors of 66 and 154? _____ [1]

3 What are the first two common multiples of 7 and 9? _____ [1]

4 Find the first two common multiples of 21 and 33 _____ [1]

5 Find two square numbers between 150 and 200 _____ [1]

6 Find two cube numbers between 400 and 900 _____ [1]

7 Find a prime number between 90 and 100 _____ [1]

9

Fractions and decimals

Examples

1 Simplify $\frac{12}{18}$.

Method:

$\frac{12}{18} = \frac{2 \times 6}{3 \times 6} = \frac{2}{3}$

2 Find the missing number.

$\frac{5}{8} = \frac{?}{24}$

Method:

$\frac{5}{8} = \frac{5 \times 3}{8 \times 3} = \frac{15}{24}$

so the missing number is 15

Ⓐ Answer these questions. You do not need to show your workings out.

1 Simplify $\frac{18}{24}$ _____ ☐ [1]

2 Simplify $\frac{15}{25}$ _____ ☐ [1]

3 Find the missing numbers. _____ , _____ ☐ [1]

$\frac{12}{15} = \frac{?}{5}$ $\qquad$ $\frac{7}{9} = \frac{?}{27}$

Examples

Which is larger, $\frac{12}{7}$ or $1\frac{11}{14}$?

Method:

Step 1
Make them both mixed numbers or **improper fractions**:

$1\frac{5}{7}$ and $1\frac{11}{14}$ $\qquad$ or $\qquad$ $\frac{12}{7}$ and $\frac{25}{14}$

Step 2
Change the fractions to have the same denominator:

$1\frac{10}{14}$ and $1\frac{11}{14}$ $\qquad$ or $\qquad$ $\frac{24}{14}$ and $\frac{25}{14}$

The answer is $1\frac{11}{14}$

Ⓑ Answer these questions. You do not need to show your workings out.

1 Which is larger, $\frac{4}{7}$ or $\frac{9}{14}$? _____ ☐ [1]

2 Which is larger, $\frac{4}{5}$ or $\frac{7}{8}$? _____ ☐ [1]

3 Which is larger, $1\frac{5}{12}$ or $1\frac{1}{3}$? _____ ☐ [1]

4 Which is larger, $\frac{29}{14}$ or $2\frac{1}{7}$? _____ ☐ [1]

7

Unit 5

Example

Place $\frac{1}{2}$, 0.3, $\frac{3}{8}$, $\frac{1}{3}$ in **descending** order.

Method:

Write them all as decimals.

$\frac{1}{2}$ = 0.5   1st

0.3   4th

$\frac{3}{8}$ = 0.375   2nd

$\frac{1}{3}$ = 0.3333...   3rd

Answer:

$\frac{1}{2}$, $\frac{3}{8}$, $\frac{1}{3}$, 0.3

ⓒ Answer these questions. You do not need to show your workings out.

1 Find $\frac{3}{5}$ as a decimal. _____ ☐ [1]

2 Find $1\frac{5}{8}$ as a decimal. _____ ☐ [1]

💡 **Helpful Hint**

Learn the common fractions in their decimal form.

$\frac{1}{8}$ = 0.125 $\frac{3}{8}$ = 0.375 $\frac{5}{8}$ = 0.625

$\frac{1}{4}$ = 0.25 $\frac{1}{2}$ = 0.5 $\frac{3}{4}$ = 0.75

$\frac{1}{3}$ = 0.3333... $\frac{2}{3}$ = 0.66666... $\frac{7}{8}$ = 0.875

---

3 Which is bigger, 0.77 or $\frac{7}{9}$? _____ ☐ [1]

4 Find $3\frac{1}{4}$ as a decimal. _____ ☐ [1]

ⓓ Answer these questions.

1 Which is the odd one out? Circle your answer.

a $\frac{6}{8}$ **b** $\frac{30}{40}$ **c** $\frac{15}{20}$ **d** $\frac{16}{24}$ **e** $\frac{3}{4}$ ☐ [1]

2 Draw lines to pair up the equivalent fractions.

$\frac{12}{24}$ $\frac{2}{7}$ $\frac{1}{4}$ $\frac{16}{20}$ $\frac{2}{6}$

$\frac{6}{18}$ $\frac{4}{5}$ $\frac{6}{21}$ $\frac{5}{10}$ $\frac{9}{36}$ ☐ [3]

◢ 8

3 True or false? Circle your answer.

If 6 out of 12 pupils are boys, then $\frac{1}{2}$ are boys. ⟶ True/False

If 8 out of 24 players wear glasses, then $\frac{1}{4}$ wear glasses. ⟶ True/False

3 of the 27 pupils were late this morning, so $\frac{1}{9}$ are late. ⟶ True/False [3]

4 Place the following fractions in descending order.

$\frac{3}{5}$ $\frac{5}{15}$ $\frac{7}{10}$ $\frac{6}{20}$ $\frac{12}{30}$

_____ [1]

5 Place the following fractions in **ascending** order.

$1\frac{3}{10}$ $\frac{25}{20}$ $1\frac{2}{5}$ $\frac{15}{10}$ $1\frac{17}{40}$

_____ [1]

6 Kate, Obi, Emily and Marcus did 4 different maths tests. Kate got $\frac{16}{18}$, Obi got $\frac{9}{12}$, Emily got $\frac{29}{36}$ and Marcus got $\frac{50}{60}$. Who got the second highest score? Show your working out.

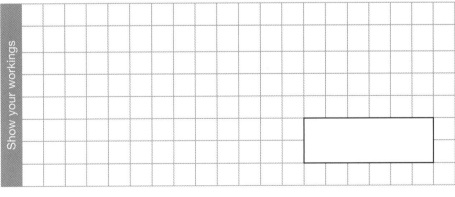

_____ [1]

7 What is $\frac{22}{40}$ as a decimal? Show your working out.

_____ [1]

7

8 If $\frac{43}{40}$ = 1.075 and $\frac{49}{40}$ = 1.225, find $\frac{52}{40}$ as a decimal. Show your working out.

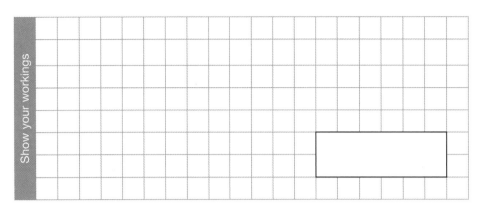

[1]

9 If a storage box is $\frac{17}{40}$ metres long, what is this in metres as a decimal? Show your working out.

m

[1]

Ⓔ Answer these questions. You do not need to show your workings out.

1 Find the missing value.

$1\frac{1}{2} = \frac{18}{?}$? = _____ [1]

2 Find the missing value.

$2\frac{?}{7} = \frac{48}{21}$? = _____ [1]

3 Place the following in descending order.

$1\frac{3}{7}$, $\frac{27}{21}$, $1\frac{14}{35}$, $\frac{99}{70}$ _____ [1]

4 Place the following in ascending order.

$\frac{121}{15}$, $7\frac{19}{20}$, $8\frac{2}{35}$, $\frac{317}{40}$, $8\frac{1}{30}$ _____ [1]

5 Place the following in descending order.

$\frac{12}{5}$, $2\frac{3}{8}$, 2.435, $\frac{49}{21}$ _____ [1]

6 Find $\frac{313}{40}$ as a decimal.   _____ [1]

8

Answers

Unit 1

(A)

1 $5x = 26$
2 $x - 6 = 14$
3 $\frac{p}{7} = 12$
4 $g - 5 = 20$
5 $6x + 10 = 560$

(B)

1 14
2 23
3 32
4 8

(C)

1 $20 \div 4 = 5\,cm$
2 Share £x between seven people. Each person gets £20. $\frac{x}{7} = 20$

   Seven apples cost 20p. $7x = 20$

   If you take 7 away from this number you get 20 $x - 7 = 20$

   In seven years' time I will be 20. $x + 7 = 20$
3 $5x + 12 = 1006$
4 $24 \times 5 = T = 120$

(D)

1 $Q = 5$
2 $R = 4.5$
3 $P = 8.9$
4 $W = 4.5 + 2.6 = 7.1$
5 25 cm. $P = 6 \times 1.5 + 16 = 25$ cm
6 94 cm. $P = 6 \times 13 + 16 = 94$ cm
7 $x = 8$ cm. Both sides are the same length, so $2x = x + 8$; subtracting x from both sides gives $x = 8$
8 16 cm. If $x = 8$, $2x = 2 \times 8 = 16$ cm; or, using the expression for the other side, $x + 8 = 8 + 8 = 16$ cm
9 64 cm. $P = 4 \times 16 = 64$ cm; or, using the original equation for P, $P = 6 \times 8 + 16 = 64$ cm
10 $P = 8x$

Unit 2

(A)

1 10, 11
2 27, 30
3 5, 3
4 16, 26
5 **e** 4, 2
6 **b** 5, 4
7 **d** 3, 2

(B)

1 13, 22
2 **b** and **e**
3 10, 22
4 5 and 16 or 7 and 13

(C)

1 -1, -3
2 11, 13.9
3 18, 24
4 **c** 6.1, 1.1
5 **a** 6.8, 2.3
6 **b** 3, 0

Unit 3

(A)

1 6.27
2 **d** 8.94
3 $30 \times £0.50 = £15$
4 22×2 hr 3 mins $\approx 20 \times 2 = 40$ hrs
5 $20.99 - 5 - 11.22 = £4.77$
6 66 (add 8 each time)

(B)

1 $25 \times 2 \times 2 \times 6 = 600$
2 $1.27 + 12 - 0.27 = 13$
3 $8.50 + 1 - 7.98 = £1.52$
4 2 hr = 120 mins so $120 - 5 - 55 - 20 = 40$ mins

(C)

1 15.72
2 $1000 \times 3000 = £3\,000\,000$
3 **a** 50.903
4 $796 - 429 - 208 - 100 = 59$
5 −29 (subtract 11 each time)

Unit 4

(A)

1 1 (no others)
2 1, 7
3 15, 30
4 24, 48
5 64, 81
6 64, 125
7 53, 59

(B)

1 11 o'clock

2 3 rows

3 36 bricks

4 11 boys

(C)

1 1, 3

2 1, 2, 11, 22

3 63, 126

4 231, 462

5 169, 196

6 512, 729

7 97

Unit 5

(A)

1 $\frac{3}{4}$

2 $\frac{3}{5}$

3 4, 21

(B)

1 $\frac{9}{14}$ $\frac{4}{7} = \frac{8}{14}$

2 $\frac{7}{8}$ $\frac{4}{5} = \frac{32}{40}$, $\frac{7}{8} = \frac{35}{40}$

3 $1\frac{5}{12}$ $1\frac{1}{3} = 1\frac{4}{12}$

4 $2\frac{1}{7}$ $2\frac{1}{7} = \frac{30}{24}$

(C)

1 0.6

2 1.625

3 $\frac{7}{9}$

4 3.25

(D)

1 d $\frac{16}{24}$

2 $\frac{12}{24} = \frac{5}{10}$, $\frac{2}{7} = \frac{6}{21}$, $\frac{1}{4} = \frac{9}{36}$, $\frac{16}{20} = \frac{4}{5}$, $\frac{2}{6} = \frac{6}{18}$

3 True, False, True

4 $\frac{7}{10} = \frac{21}{30}$, $\frac{3}{5} = \frac{18}{30}$, $\frac{12}{30}$ $\frac{5}{15} = \frac{10}{30}$, $\frac{6}{20} = \frac{9}{30}$

5 $\frac{25}{20} = \frac{50}{40}$, $1\frac{3}{10} = \frac{13}{10} = \frac{52}{14}$, $1\frac{2}{5} = \frac{7}{5} = \frac{56}{40}$,

$1\frac{17}{40} = \frac{57}{40}$, $\frac{15}{10} = \frac{60}{40}$

6 Kate $\frac{16}{18} = \frac{32}{36}$, Obi $\frac{9}{12} = \frac{27}{36}$, Emily $\frac{29}{36}$, **Marcus**

$\frac{50}{60} = \frac{5}{6} = \frac{30}{36}$, so Marcus got the second highest score.

7 0.55

8 1.3

9 0.425 m

(E)

1 12

2 2

3 $1\frac{3}{7}$, $\frac{99}{70}$, $1\frac{14}{35}$, $\frac{27}{21}$

4 $\frac{121}{15}$, $8\frac{2}{35}$, $8\frac{1}{30}$, $7\frac{19}{20}$, $\frac{317}{40}$

5 2.435, $\frac{12}{5} = 2.4$, $2\frac{3}{8} = 2.375$, $\frac{49}{21} = 2.3333...$

6 7.825

Unit 6

(A)

1 15.042 ≈ 15.04

2 7.986 ≈ 8.0

3 1.875 ≈ 1.88

4 $\frac{22}{100} = \frac{11}{50}$

5 27%

6 $\frac{54}{100} = 0.54$

(B)

1 109.4p × 13 = 1422.2p ≈ £14.22

2 1 − 0.25 − 0.60 = 0.15 = 15%

3 £576.79 ÷ 25 = £23.07; 25 × £23.07 = £576.75;
so each pupil has £23.07 and there is 4p left over

4 12.71

(C)

1 7.854 ≈ 7.85

2 8.36 ≈ 8.4

3 0.198181... ≈ 0.20

4 $\frac{56}{100} = \frac{4 \times 14}{4 \times 25} = \frac{14}{25}$

5 9%

6 $\frac{27}{20} = \frac{5 \times 27}{5 \times 20} = \frac{135}{100} = 1.35$

Unit 7

(A)

1 2 307 506

2 7 000 000

3 c, b, a, d

4 CDLXIX

5 500 + 100 + 100 + 90 + 1 = 791

6 CCXC + I + 4 = DCCXC + V = DCCXCV

7 1022-3 = 1019 = M + X + IX = MXIX

B

1 CMXCIII = CM + XC + III = 900 + 90 + 3 = 993
2 seven hundred thousand, four hundred
3 smallest = CMXXXIII = 933; largest = MCX = 1110
4 1 010 100 – 101 010 = 909 090 = nine hundred and nine thousand and ninety

C

1 9 070 006
2 ninety thousand
3 **d, a, b, c**
4 CMXLIX
5 2049
6 997 + 4 = 1,001 = MI
7 1002 – 3 = 999 = CMXCIX

Unit 8

A

1 £671 000
2 40 000
3 63 200 000
4 –2°C
5 39
6 5
7 2

B

1 32 200
2 8
3 15°C
4 8

C

1 £1 000 000
2 130 000
3 –2.6, –2, –1.4, 1, 1.5, 5
4 38
5 95
6 20 + 35 = 55. 10 boxes
7 8

Unit 9

A

1 1:2
2 5:2

3 £60
4 **b** 31:63

B

1 60%
2 £24
3 40%
4 £11.50

C

1 £12
2 2:3
3 1:4 = 18:72 and 72 ÷ 12 = 6, so each player gets £6
4 4:7 = 12:21, 1:5 = 21:105, 2:5 = 6:15, 5:8 = 15:24
5 15% of 360 = 54 and 55% of 106 = 55.33, so B is bigger
6 65% of 260 = 169
7 R, P, T, S, Q:P = £45, Q = £60, R = £44, S = £55, T = £48

D

1 1:5
2 £161.60:£163.20; 101 + 102 = 203, 203 × 1.6 = 324.80
3 (Work backwards) 2:1 = Pat has 12, Rhianna has 6. Rhianna gives the sweet back. Pat has 11, Rhianna has 7. They eat a sweet. Pat has 12, Rhianna has 8. Pat gives Rhianna a sweet. Pat has 13, Rhianna has 7. Total = 13 + 7 = 20
4 4.37
5 F; F = £110.40, G = £109.98
6 21.16; first find 50% of 92 then find 46% of 46

Unit 10

A

1 12 cm
2 1.5
3 4.5 cm
4 25
5 £700
6 6:5

B

1 9.1 ÷ 14 × 12 = 7.8 cm
2 50 ÷ 5 = 10 so 10x = (3 + x + 9) so x = 1
3 5 cm:15 km = 1 cm:3 km = 1:3000, so the scale factor is 3000
4 4:5 = 9 so 27 ÷ 9 × 5 = 15

Ⓒ

1 5.25 cm

2 $10.5 \div 14 = \frac{3}{4}$

3 $2 \times 12.5 \div 7.5 = 3.3333.... \text{ m} \approx 333 \text{ cm}$

4 $21 \div 3 \times (10 + 3 + 3) = 7 \times 16 = 112$

5 $1000 \div (2 + 3 + 7) \times 3 = 250$, £250

6 $93 \div 6 \times 11 = 170.5 \text{ cm}$

Decimals and percentages

Examples

1 Round 2.18054 to the following degree of accuracy:

a) to 1 decimal place

b) to 2 decimal places

c) to 3 decimal places.

Method:

a) This would be 2.1 to 1 decimal place, but the next digit is greater than 4 so we need to round 2.1 up to **2.2**

b) This would be 2.18 to 2 decimal places, but the next digit is **not** greater than 4 so we do **not** need to round 2.18 up to 2.19. The answer is **2.18**

c) This would be 2.180 to 3 decimal places, but the next digit is greater than 4 so we need to round 2.180 up to **2.181**

2 Complete the following table:

Fraction	Decimal	Percentage
$\frac{1}{2}$	0.5	50%
$\frac{1}{4}$		
	0.3	
		80%

Method:

Find $\frac{1}{2}, \frac{1}{4}, \frac{1}{8}$ by repeated halving. Do the same for the decimals and **percentages**.

$\frac{1}{2} = 0.5 = 50\%$

$\frac{1}{4} = 0.25 = 25\%$

$\frac{1}{8} = 0.125 = 12.5\%$

Also know that

$\frac{1}{10} = 0.1 = 10\%$

and if you again divide by 10 you get

$\frac{1}{100} = 0.01 = 1\%$

So

Fraction	Decimal	Percentage
$\frac{1}{2}$	0.5	50%
$\frac{1}{4}$	0.25	25%
$\frac{3}{10}$	0.3	30%
$\frac{8}{10}$	0.8	80%

Unit 6

(A) Answer these questions. You do not need to show your workings out.

1 Find 3 × 5.014. Give your answer to 2 decimal places. _____ [1]

2 Find 13 – 5.014. Give your answer to 1 decimal place. _____ [1]

3 Find 15 ÷ 8. Give your answer to 2 decimal places. _____ [1]

4 Find 22% as a fraction. _____ [1]

5 What is 0.27 as a percentage? _____ [1]

6 Find $\frac{27}{50}$ as a decimal. _____ [1]

(B) Answer these questions and show your workings out.

1

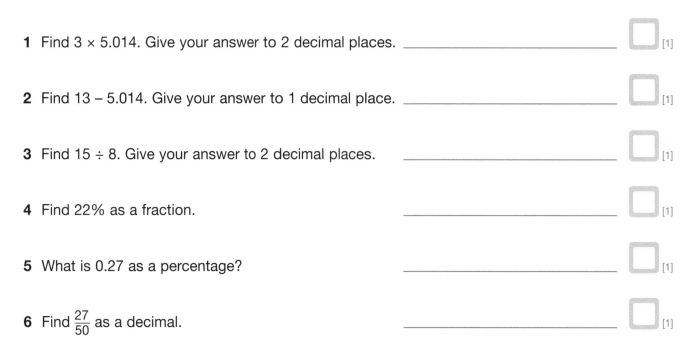

petrol - 109.4p

A litre of petrol costs 109.4p. If we put 13 litres in the car, how much will we need to pay in pounds and pence?

Show your workings

£ _____ . _____

[1]

/ 7

2 If I have $\frac{1}{4}$ of a cake and my sister has 0.6, what percentage is left for my brother?

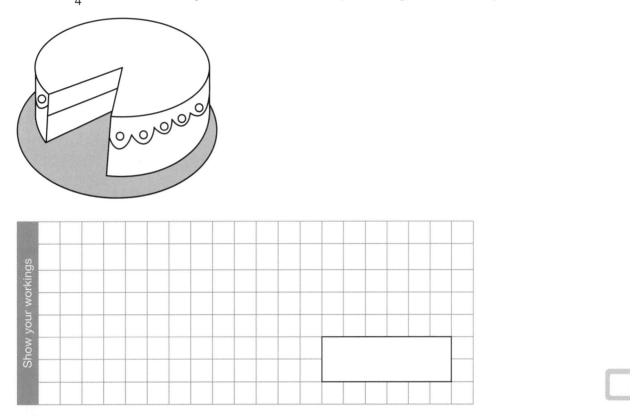

Show your workings

[1]

3 The spending money left over from our Year 6 residential trip was split equally between all 25 pupils. The total amount to share out was £576.79.

How much does each pupil receive and how many pence are left?

Each pupil gets £ _____ . _____

There is _____ p left over.

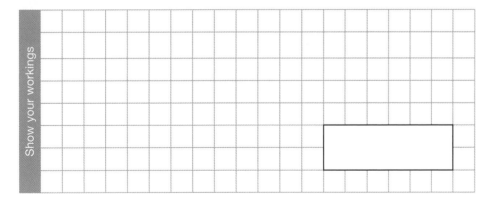

Show your workings

[2]

3

Unit 6

4 Finn works out the area of a room to be 12.7082 m².

What is the area to two decimal places?

Show your workings

m²

[1]

ⓒ Answer these questions. You do not need to show your workings out.

1 Find 2.1 × 3.74. Give your answer to 2 decimal places. _____ [1]

2 Find 12.1 − 3.74. Give your answer to 1 decimal place. _____ [1]

3 Find 2.18 ÷ 11. Give your answer to 2 decimal places. _____ [1]

4 Find 56% as a fraction in its simplest form. _____ [1]

5 What is 0.09 as a percentage? _____ [1]

6 Find $\frac{27}{20}$ as a decimal. _____ [1]

7

Number and place value

Examples

1 Find the value of the following digits in the number 8 017 529

a 1

b 5

c 2

Method:

Numbers are batched in "threes" starting from the right.

…, millions, thousands, units

so 8 017 529 is eight **million**, seventeen **thousand**, five hundred and twenty-nine.

Answers:

a 1 is ten thousand = 10 000

b 5 is five hundred = 500

c 2 is twenty = 20

2 Place the following in **ascending** order:

XCII   CXII   CIX

Method:

Roman numerals are read from the left and looking for the highest value first.

M	D	C	L	X	V	I
1000	500	100	50	10	5	1

If your number is one principal unit (any of those in bold) less than one of the units above, it is placed to the LEFT of that unit. For example, 90 would be made by placing **X** (10) before **C** (100), so **XC**, which means "10 less than 100".

CM	CD	XC	XL	IX	IV
900	400	90	40	9	4

Otherwise the unit goes to the right, up to a maximum of 3 identical symbols at a time.

MMM	DCC	CC	LX	XXX	VIII
3000	700	200	60	30	8

Numbers are then built from the left to the right.

Answers:

XCII = XC + II = 90 + 2 = 92

CXII = C + X + II = 100 + 10 + 2 = 112

CIX = C + IX = 100 + 9 = 109

So the order is XCII, CIX, CXII.

Unit 7

(A) Answer these questions. You do not need to show your workings out.

1 Write two million, three hundred and seven thousand, five hundred and six in digits.

_____ [1]

2 What is the value of the seven in 7 012 008?

_____ [1]

3 Place the following in descending order:

  a Two hundred thousand and seven

  b 207 000

  c 270 002

  d Twenty seven thousand and twenty seven

_____ [1]

4 Write 469 in Roman numerals.

_____ [1]

5 Write DCCXCI in digits.

_____ [1]

6 Write four more than DCCXCI in Roman numerals.

_____ [1]

7 What is three less than MXXII in Roman numerals?

_____ [1]

7

B Answer these questions and show your workings out.

1

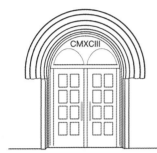

Write the year written above the doorway in digits.

[1]

2 The speed of light is 299 792 458 metres per second.

What are the values of the seven and the four in words?

Seven represents _____ .

Four represents _____ .

[2]

3 Which of the following numbers is the smallest and which is the largest?

CMXXXIII   1001   MCX   941

smallest is _____

largest is _____

[2]

5

4 Write the value of the following sum in words:

1 010 100 minus one hundred and one thousand and ten.

_____

Show your workings

_____ [1]

(c) Answer these questions. You do not need to show your workings out.

1 Write nine million, seventy thousand and six in digits.

_____ [1]

2 What is the value of the nine in 7 090 062 in words?

_____ [1]

3 Place the following in ascending order:
   a Two million, eight thousand and thirty-nine
   b 2 008 309
   c 2 080 030
   d two hundred and eighty thousand, three hundred and ninety

_____ [1]

4 Write 949 in Roman numerals.

_____ [1]

5 Write MMXLIX in digits.

_____ [1]

6 Write four more than CMXCVII in Roman numerals.

_____ [1]

7 What is three less than MII in Roman numerals?

_____ [1]

8

Approximation and rounding

Examples

1 Round 234 567 to the following:

a to the nearest 10
b to the nearest 1 000
c to the nearest 100 000

Method:

Think about the amount being on a number line marked with the units to be rounded to.

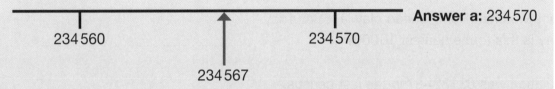

Answer a: 234 570

Mark the number on the line to see which number on the number line is closer. Remember that if it is in the middle (5) you round it up!

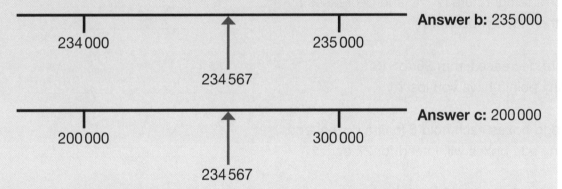

Answer b: 235 000

Answer c: 200 000

2 This morning it was -2°C. The temperature has now increased by 5°C. What is the new temperature?

Method:

Think about or sketch a number line with 0 in the middle:

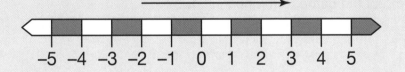

Start at –2 and then go up 5 to get to +3.

Answer: 3°C.

3 A minibus can carry 17 children. There are 60 pupils to transport. How many trips will the minibus have to make in order to transport all the pupils?

> **Method:**
>
> Divide 60 by 17
> If it is not a whole number then you will need to round **UP** otherwise you will end up leaving some of the pupils behind!
> 60 ÷ 17 = 3, so you need **4** trips.
>
> **Answer:** 4.

Ⓐ Answer these questions. You do not need to show your workings out.

1 Round £670 824 to the nearest £1000.   £ _____ [1]

2 39 245 fans watched Bond United play last Saturday.
How many is this to the nearest 10 000?   _____ [1]

3 The population was 63 182 487 in the last census.
What is this to the nearest one hundred thousand?   _____ [1]

4 The fridge's temperature is 7°C and decreases by 9°C.
What is the new temperature?   _____ [1]

5 Your score decreases from 26 to -13.
How many points have you lost?   _____ [1]

6 Several egg boxes each hold 6 (half a dozen) eggs.
How many egg boxes will I need for 27 eggs?   _____ [1]

7 I have made 46 identical birthday cards.
I need to supply 6 packs, each containing 8 cards.
How many more cards do I need to make?   _____ [1]

Ⓑ Answer these questions.

1 At a football game there are 32 173 home supporters and 5217 away supporters.
How many home supporters attended the game to the nearest 100?

Show your workings

[1]

8

2 Julius was born in MMIX.

How old was he on his birthday in MMXVII?

Show your workings

| years old |

[1]

3 Winter tyres are ideal for driving at temperatures of +7°C and below.

The coldest temperature in Bondville last winter was –8°C.

What is the difference in temperature from the warmest to the coldest day that winter tyres could be used last year in Bondville?

Show your workings

| °C |

[1]

4 The 29 pupils in class 6B are queuing up to go on a roller-coaster ride.

Each carriage takes a maximum of 4 people.

What is the minimum number of carriages they require?

Show your workings

[1]

3

ⓒ Answer these questions. You do not need to show your workings out.

1 Round £960 004 to the nearest £100 000

_____ [1]

2 129 504 people watched the opening ceremony of the last games.

How many is this to the nearest 10 000?

_____ [1]

3 Place these numbers in ascending order:

5, –2.6, 1.5, –2, 1, –1.4

_____ [1]

4 What is the missing number?

$-80 + \cdots = -42$

_____ [1]

5 What is the missing number?

$-80 + \cdots + 10 = 25$

_____ [1]

6 I have four packs of five sweets and five packs of seven sweets. I need to put them

into boxes. Each box holds a maximum of six packs of sweets.

How many boxes do I need?

_____ [1]

7 A school needs to transport all 356 pupils to a special event by coach. Each coach

can carry 52 passengers but 3 of the passengers need to be teachers.

How many coaches are needed to transport all the pupils?

_____ [1]

7

Ratio and relative sizes

Examples

1 Simplify, as a **ratio**, £12 to £18

　　　　　　12:18

Method:

Divide both sides by the highest common factor: **6**

　　　　　　12 ÷ **6**:18 ÷ **6**

Answer:　　　　2:3

2 Sweets are shared between John and Sue in the ratio 3:4

If John takes 30 sweets how many does Sue take?

　　　　　　　　　3:4

Method:

Multiply both sides by the same number (**10**) to make John's 3 into 30

　　　　　　　　3 × **10**:4 × 10

　　　　　　　　　30:40

Answer: Sue takes 40 sweets.

Ⓐ Answer these questions. You do not need to show your workings out.

1 Simplify the ratio 7:14　　　　　　　　　_____:_____ ☐ [1]

2 Write the ratio 15:6 in simplified form.　　_____:_____ ☐ [1]

3 Prize money is shared between Hillview School and
Forest School in the ratio 2:3
If Hillview School wins £40, how much does
Forest School receive?　　　　　　　　£ _____ ☐ [1]

💡 Helpful Hint

　　　2:5
10 × 2:5 × **10**
　　　20:50　　　　When changing quantities:
20 ÷ **5**:50 ÷ **5**
　　　4:10　　　　**1** Make sure you change both values at the same time.
　　　　　　　　2 Only use multiplication or division. Never add or subtract!

4 Which ratio is **not** the same as 1:2?

　　a 12:24　　**b** 31:63　　**c** 0.5:1　　**d** 150:300　　**e** 12.6:25.2

☐ [1]

◁ 4

Unit 9

Examples

1 Find 15% of £70
Method:

Either do 0.15 × 70 =10.5
Or find 10% the 5% and add the
result

$$10\% = £7$$
$$5\% = £3.50$$
Answer: 15% = £10.50

2 What is 13 out of 20 as a percentage?
Method:

Either do 13 × **100** ÷ 20
Or find the equivalent fraction to $\frac{13}{20}$
with denominator 100

$$\frac{13}{20} = \frac{13 \times 5}{20 \times 5} = \frac{65}{100}$$

Answer: 65%

Ⓑ Answer these questions. You do not need to show your workings out.

1 Write the score 6 out of 10 as a percentage. _____% ☐ [1]

2 What is 30% of £80? £_____% ☐ [1]

3 Write the score 6 out of 15 as a percentage. _____% ☐ [1]

4 What is 23% of £50? £_____% ☐ [1]

Ⓒ Answer these questions.

1 £20 is shared between Brian and Adam in the ratio 2:3

How much does Adam receive? Show your working out.

Show your workings

£

☐ [1]

5

2 A batch of purple paint is made by mixing $\frac{1}{3}$ litre of blue paint with $\frac{1}{2}$ litre of red paint.

Simplify the ratio blue:red and show your working out.

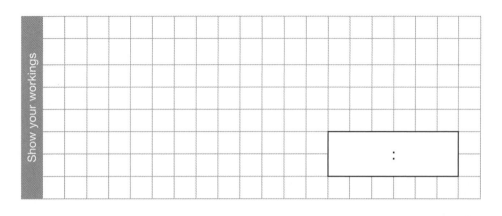

[1]

3 The local football team wins £90 in prize money.

The team and the manager share the prize in the ratio 4:1

The 12 players share their prize money equally.

How much does each player get? Show your working out.

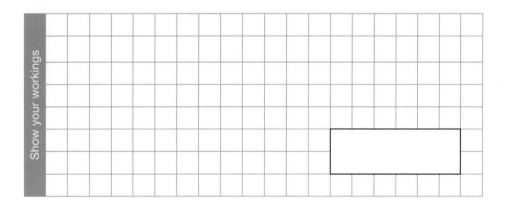

[1]

4 Pair up the equivalent ratios by drawing a line between each pair.

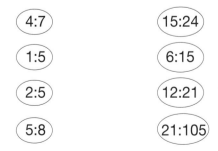

4:7	15:24
1:5	6:15
2:5	12:21
5:8	21:105

[4]

6

💡 **Helpful Hint**

If you are finding the larger proportion, then the bigger the percentage, the larger the proportion. So find the percentage of each value.

5 Which is bigger? Circle your answer.

A	B
15% of £360	55% of £106

[1]

6 50% of the pupils at Grange Park School are girls and there are 130 of them.
35% of the pupils walk to school.
How many pupils do **not** walk to school? _____

[1]

7 Place the following amounts in ascending order.

P	Q	R	S	T
20% of £225	15% of £400	10% of £440	5% of £1100	30% of £160

1st _____	2nd _____	3rd _____	4th _____	5th _____

[1]

Ⓓ Answer these questions. You do not need to show your workings out.

1 Simplify the ratio 4:20   _____ : _____ [1]

2 Share £324.80 in the ratio 101:102   £ _____ : £ _____ [1]

3 Pat and Rhianna are sharing their sweets.
Pat gives Rhianna one of her sweets and the ratio is now 3:2
They each eat a sweet and the ratio becomes 11:7
Rhianna now gives Pat the sweet back. They now have
sweets in the ratio 2:1
Pat now has 12 sweets.
How many did they have in total to share at the beginning?   _____ [1]

4 Find 23% of 19   _____ [1]

5 Which is larger?

F	G
92% of £120	94% of £117

_____ [1]

6 What is 46% of 50% of £92?   £ _____ [1]

9

Proportion and scale factors

Similar shapes have all corresponding angles equal. All the corresponding lengths have the same **scale factor**.

Examples

1 Find the height of the smaller box of cornflakes. The two boxes are similar.

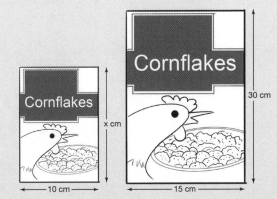

2 Share £45 between Ann, Ben and Carol in the ratio 2:3:4
How much does each receive?

Method:

Find the total of the ratios:
A:B:C
2:3:4 = 9
What do you multiply 9 by to get 45? The answer is 5
2 × 5:3 × 5:4 × 5 = 9 × 5
10:15:20
Answer: Ann gets £10, Ben gets £15 and Carol gets £20

(A) Answer these questions. You do not need to show your workings out.

1

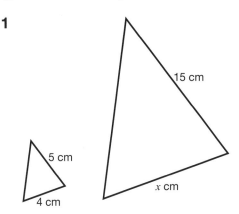

The two triangles are similar. Find the missing length x cm.

_____ [1]

1

2 What is the scale factor of two similar rectangles if the lengths are 12 cm and 18 cm?

_____ [1]

3 Two similar bottles have heights of 16 cm and 8 cm. What is the width of the smaller bottle if the larger bottle is 9 cm?

_____ [1]

4 Amar and Zara share their sweets in the ratio 5:4
If Zara gets 20 sweets, how many does Amar get?

_____ [1]

5 £1000 prize money is shared in the ratio 3:7
How much is the larger prize?

_____ [1]

6 Mick is 18 years old and Leanne is 15 years old. What is their age as a simplified ratio?

_____ [1]

(B) Answer these questions and show your workings out.

1

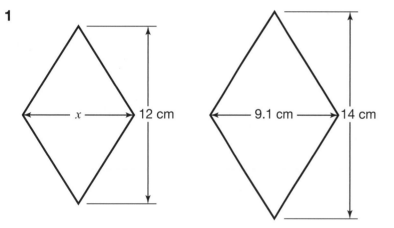

Find the width of the smaller rhombus in cm.

Show your workings

cm [1]

6

2 Harry, Beth and Kieran share £50 in the ratio 3:x:6
   If Beth gets £5 what is the value of x?

Show your workings

[1]

3 The distance between the towns of Bond and Castleton on a map is 5 cm
   and the distance on the ground is 15 km.

   Find the scale factor of enlargement from map to ground.

Show your workings

[1]

4 The ratio of girls to boys in class 6B is 4:5. If the number of pupils is 27,
   how many boys are in 6B?

Show your workings

[1]

3

ⓒ Answer these questions. You do not need to show your workings out.

1

7 cm

12 cm

_x_ cm

9 cm

The two parallelograms are similar. Find the value of _x_.

_____ cm [1]

2 What is the scale factor of two similar squares if the lengths are 14 cm and 10.5 cm? Find the answer as a simplified fraction.

_____ [1]

3 Two similar containers have widths of 12.5 m and 7.5 m. If the smaller container is 2 m tall, how tall is the larger container in cm to the nearest cm?

_____ cm [1]

4 Barney, Felix and Lara share their biscuits in the ratio 10:3:3. If Lara got 21 biscuits, how many did they have to share?

_____ [1]

5 £1000 prize money is shared in the ratio 2:3:7
How much is the middle prize?

£ _____ [1]

6 The heights of three pupils are in the ratio 8:6:11. If the shortest pupil is 0.93 m in height, how tall is the tallest pupil in cm?

_____ cm [1]

6

Key Words

$\approx$ means approximately equal to and is sometimes used when rounding values

algebraically using letters to represent unknown values

ascending increasing or getting bigger

descending going down or getting smaller

factors the numbers of a given value which will divide into it without a remainder

improper fraction (vulgar fraction) fraction with the numerator larger than the denominator

multiples the original number multiplied by 1 or 2 or 3 or 4 etc

percentage a fraction out of 100, expressed as %

perimeter the total distance around a shape

prime number a number with exactly two factors, 1 and itself

ratio how many of the first object are equal to how many of the second object

scale factor where corresponding sides of two objects have the same ratio, and that the smaller can be multiplied by the same scale factor

sequence an order of numbers which follows a fixed pattern from term to term

term a number or value in a sequence

Progress chart

Bond SATs Skills Maths Workbook – Numbers 10–11

How did you do? Fill in your score below and shade in the corresponding boxes to compare your progress across the different tests and units.

50%   100%   50%   100%

Unit 1, p3 Score __ / 5

Unit 1, p4 Score __ / 5

Unit 1, p5 Score __ / 6

Unit 1, p6 Score __ / 10

Unit 2, p8 Score __ / 13

Unit 2, p9 Score __ / 3

Unit 2, p10 Score __ / 11

Unit 3, p11 Score __ / 4

Unit 3, p12 Score __ / 4

Unit 3, p13 Score __ / 2

Unit 3, p14 Score __ / 5

Unit 4, p15 Score __ / 4

Unit 4, p16 Score __ / 4

Unit 4, p17 Score __ / 2

Unit 4, p18 Score __ / 9

Unit 5, p19 Score __ / 7

Unit 5, p20 Score __ / 8

Unit 5, p21 Score __ / 7

Unit 5, p22 Score __ / 8

Unit 6, p28 Score __ / 7

Unit 6, p29, Score __ / 3

Unit 6, p30, Score __ / 7

Unit 7, p32, Score __ / 7

Unit 7, p33, Score __ / 5

Unit 7, p34, Score __ / 8

Unit 8, p36, Score __ / 8

Unit 8, p37, Score __ / 3

Unit 8, p38, Score __ / 7

Unit 9, p39, Score __ / 4

Unit 9, p40, Score __ / 5

Unit 9, p41, Score __ / 6

Unit 9, p42, Score __ / 9

Unit 10, p43, Score __ / 1

Unit 10, p44, Score __ / 6

Unit 10, p45, Score __ / 3

Unit 10, p46, Score __ / 6